The Adventures Of Junk Food Dude

Written by Robyn Openshaw

Illustrated by Lori Sume

The Adventures of Junk Food Dude

Published by Robyn Openshaw/GreenSmoothieGirl.com
Lindon, UT
First Printing October 2010

For information regarding permission, please email:
support123@greensmoothiegirl.com

ISBN 978-0-9831113-0-6

Printed in China

Dedicated to Kincade, Emma, Mary Elizabeth, and Tennyson

You're the four reasons I learned all this stuff,
and I will adore you forever.

Once there was a boy
who loved climbing trees.

He loved running fast.

He pitched on a baseball
team after school.

The boy ate lots of fruits and vegetables.

He blended a drink every day with greens and fruit.
Like spinach and bananas. Or kale and peaches.

People called him Green Smoothie Guy.

A kid in his class wanted to do those things, too. But he couldn't.

W hen he ran, he couldn't breathe.

H e couldn't pull himself up into the tree on the playground.

He ate school lunch: pizza, chicken nuggets, & hot dogs.

After school, he watched TV and ate chips, cookies, and candy.

People called him Junk Food Dude.

CHIPS

Green Smoothie Guy ate colorful, healthy foods.
Like sweet potatoes, strawberries, avocados, and split peas.

He brought his green drink to school.

Sometimes people laughed at that, but he didn't mind.
Because they always wanted to be on his team.

He ate steamed vegetables with brown rice.

He ate brown bread sandwiches.

He ate plums, yellow bell peppers, and baby carrots.

Green Smoothie Guy had rosy cheeks and a skip in his step. Sometimes he did cartwheels just because he felt peppy!

Junk Food Dude's skin was gray. He stayed home from school a lot because he got sick.

Junk Food Dude **never** ate pretty
orange, red, or green foods.
He ate no fruits or vegetables,
unless you count ketchup!

Instead, he ate greasy, sugary foods made
with fake colors and chemicals.
French fries, caramel corn, and cheese curls.

His food came from fast food drive-thrus.
And bags, boxes, and cans.

Ramen noodles and gummy bears.

Nachos and sodas.
Sugary cookies and salty crackers.

Green Smoothie Guy was a top student in his class.
He earned A's on his report card.

He came to school ready to learn after a healthy breakfast.

He got up early to practice the piano.

He was one of the first chosen for teams
at recess because he was quick.

Green Smoothie Guy was happy most of the time.

His classmates loved how energetic and fun he was.

So when he did something,
other kids did it, too.

Junk Food Dude ate candy and donuts for breakfast.

These foods tasted good in his mouth.
But they made him tired. He got tummy aches and headaches.

He felt discouraged. "I can't do it," he thought,
watching kids playing baseball.

So he didn't try.

Every year he got chubbier.

Other kids didn't want to play with him
because he couldn't keep up.

Donuts and candy didn't have
the nutrients his body needed,
so he got hungry again
an hour after breakfast.
So he'd eat more junk food.
Like baloney sandwiches
on white bread with mayonnaise.

It was hard to run or even walk fast.
So he didn't do many fun things.

Junk Food Dude
wasn't very happy.

Green Smoothie Guy noticed that Junk Food Dude was alone a lot.

Junk Food Dude was grumpy and shy.

He was used to being laughed at and rejected by the other kids.

Green Smoothie Guy could tell that
Junk Food Dude needed a friend.

He slipped him a note in class.

It said, "Meet me after school?
I want to hang out with you."

Green Smoothie Guy walked home after school with Junk Food Dude.

They shot hoops in the driveway.

Junk Food Dude didn't usually go outside for more than a few minutes, but he had fun.

The sunshine and fresh air felt good.

16

Next day at recess, Green Smoothie Guy picked
Junk Food Dude for his basketball team.

His friends looked at him like he was crazy.

Green Smoothie Guy didn't care.

It was fun seeing a smile on Junk Food Dude's face!

17

At Green Smoothie Guy's house,
Junk Food Dude saw foods
he'd never eaten before.

He wanted to try
them, too.
At first he didn't
like them.

Green Smoothie Guy said, "They don't taste good because
you eat sugar every day. Try not eating sugar for four days.
Then good foods will taste great!"

At Junk Food Dude's house,
almost everything had sugar,
chemicals, and food dye in it.

He had to read food labels.
He didn't eat corn syrup, sugar, or aspartame.
Or monosodium glutamate or colorings.
Or ingredients he couldn't pronounce.

Those four days were really hard.

PRETZEL PIECES
MONOSODIUM GLUTAMATE, SALT, ETC.

CHEEZ CHEWS

SALTY SOUP

FRUIT PUFFS
INGREDIE
SUGAR
MSG, WH

SUGAR SYRUP

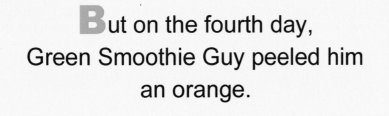

But on the fourth day,
Green Smoothie Guy peeled him
an orange.

"*Now* try it,"
he said.

The orange tasted like heaven!
So juicy!

"That's because now your body
isn't so used to eating things
that are too sweet,"
Green Smoothie Guy told him.

After a week, Junk Food Dude was noticing
something interesting. He had more energy.
He didn't want to eat donuts for breakfast.

He asked his Mom to buy
bananas and to help
him make oatmeal.

Suddenly he didn't feel grumpy in math class!

He could concentrate on the lesson.

He was enjoying school and learning more!

$5+7=12$

He was making new friends.

At first, they weren't sure about him.

But as they saw that Green Smoothie Guy
was serious about being Junk
Food Dude's friend, they were too.

After a few weeks, more strange things happened to Junk Food Dude.

His pants were too big.

He could run without getting tired.

Every morning when he woke up, he felt excited about playing basketball on the playground.

At Green Smoothie Guy's house,
it was always a fun game to put different things
in the blender to make their healthy drink.

Sometimes it was celery and parsley.

Sometimes peaches and
cantaloupe and chard.

Sometimes beets and flax seeds.

Green Smoothie Guy said that's how he got so much energy.
That's why he was almost always happy,
because he fed his body
and mind healthy foods.

Food from the
garden instead of
the drive-thru.

Junk Food Dude's mom and dad were amazed!
He didn't just look better. He felt better, too.

His parents watched and copied what he did.
They quit eating donuts and threw away the candy.

His mom made oatmeal with raisins,
cinnamon, and walnuts.

Junk Food Dude didn't want school lunch.
He asked his dad to make him a brown bread sandwich with honey
and almond butter. And an apple and bag of carrots.

One day, his dad started to
make the same lunch for himself, too.

Everybody was excited when
they felt and looked better as
they ate better.

On Saturdays, they
went for a bike ride
instead of
watching TV.

Almond Butter

When Spring arrived, Junk Food Dude's parents had to buy him all new clothes.

He wasn't chubby. His skin was clear and his eyes bright.

He woke up in the morning and jumped out of bed.

His mom didn't have to wake him up over and over.

Junk Food Dude had new friends because
he could run, climb, and play.

He smiled and laughed a lot.

In fact, no one called him
Junk Food Dude anymore.
Kids in his class started calling
him by his real name.

Hi,
Connor

He rode his bike
to school in the
mornings, excited
to learn something
new and play
with friends.

One day, Connor saw a boy
named Enrique eating lunch by himself.

He knew just what to do.
He ate lunch with Enrique and invited
him home after school.

Connor's whole life had changed.

He had learned how to be healthy.
Eating greens and vegetables and fruits.
Eating nuts and seeds, beans, and whole grains.

Connor wanted to be a friend
and good example to someone else.

He decided to teach Enrique
one thing at a time.

Starting with a good
after-school snack!

Facts about Green Smoothie Guys & Girls:

Kids who eat lots of greens, vegetables and fruits,
beans and whole grains, and nuts and seeds
have many advantages.

They are better at sports. They don't drink soda
which steals oxygen from their red blood cells.
So they can run faster, throw harder,
and play longer than kids who
do drink soda and eat candy.

They do better in school. They don't have sugar
making them first hyper and later tired and foggy.
They can think and focus because sugar
isn't making them grumpy.

They don't get sick as often.
When healthy eaters do get sick,
it's a mild cold that lasts for only a day or two.

They grow to their full height
because healthy foods
help you grow.

They have rosy skin.
And they are at just the
right weight.

Are you a Green Smoothie Guy or a Junk Food Dude?

Can you identify which foods Green Smoothie Guy would eat and which foods Junk Food Dude would eat?

lots of water

hot dogs, corn dogs, bacon, sausage, baloney

chicken nuggets

vegetables like bell peppers, carrots, cucumbers, tomatoes, beets, turnips, onions

mayonnaise, margarine, shortening, vegetable oil

cookies

greens

white bread

cake

cheese and ice cream

candy

fruits like apples, oranges, bananas, peaches, plums, nectarines, cantaloupe, watermelon, pears

soda and energy drinks

pizza

chips

seeds like pumpkin, sunflower, flax, chia, sesame

whole-wheat bread rolled oats, rye, millet

legumes like black or pinto beans, garbanzo beans, lentils, split peas

To make all the fun things that Green Smoothie Guy and Junk Food Dude whipped up in their kitchens, see

Junk Food Dude's
Yummy HEALTHY Recipes
at
http://www.greensmoothiegirl.com/junk-food-dude-recipes/

ANSWERS:
JUNK FOOD DUDE

- Chicken nuggets
- Candy
- Cookies
- Pizza
- White bread
- Cake
- **Chips**
- Soda and energy drinks
- Cheese and ice cream
- Mayonnaise, margarine, shortening, vegetable oil
- Hot dogs, corn dogs, bacon, sausage, and baloney

To make all the fun things that Green Smoothie Guy and Junk Food Dude whipped up in their kitchens, see

Junk Food Dude's
Yummy HEALTHY Recipes

at

http://www.greensmoothiegirl.com/junk-food-dude-recipes/